GRAPHIC LIBRARY™

GRAPHIC SCIENCE

A REFRESHING LOOK AT RENEWABLE ENERGY

with MAX AXIOM SUPER SCIENTIST

Katherine Krohn

illustrated by Cynthia Martin and Barbara Schulz

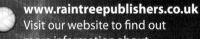

www.raintreepublishers.co.uk
Visit our website to find out
more information about
Raintree books.

To order:
☎ Phone +44 (0) 1865 888066
🖹 Fax +44 (0) 1865 314091
🖳 Visit www.raintreepublishers.co.uk

Raintree is an imprint of Capstone Global Library Limited, a company incorporated in England and
Wales having its registered office at 7 Pilgrim Street, London EC4V 6LB
Registered company number: 6695882

"Raintree" is a registered trademark of Pearson Education Limited, under licence to Capstone Global
Library Limited

Text © Capstone Press 2008
First published by Capstone Press in 2008
First published in hardback in the United Kingdom by Capstone Global Library in 2010
The moral rights of the proprietor have been asserted.

ISBN 978 1 406 21463 5 (hardback)
14 13 12 11 10

British Library Cataloguing in Publication Data
Krohn, Katherine E.
Renewable energy. -- (Graphic science)
333.7'94-dc22
A full catalogue record for this book is available from the British Library.

Designer: Alison Thiele
Cover Artist: Tod Smith
Colourists: Krista Ward and Matt Webb
UK Editor: Diyan Leake
UK Production: Alison Parsons
Originated by Capstone Global Library
Printed and bound in China by South China Printing Company Limited

Disclaimer
All the Internet addresses (URLs) given in this book were valid at the time of going to press.
However, due to the dynamic nature of the Internet, some addresses may have changed, or sites may
have changed or ceased to exist since publication. While the publisher regrets any inconvenience this
may cause readers, no responsibility for any such changes can be accepted by the publisher.

CONTENTS

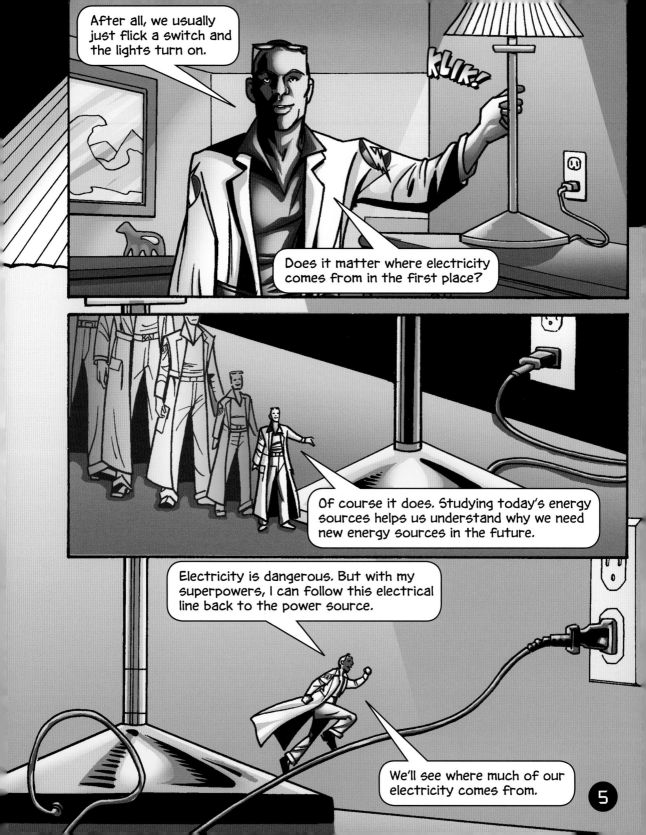

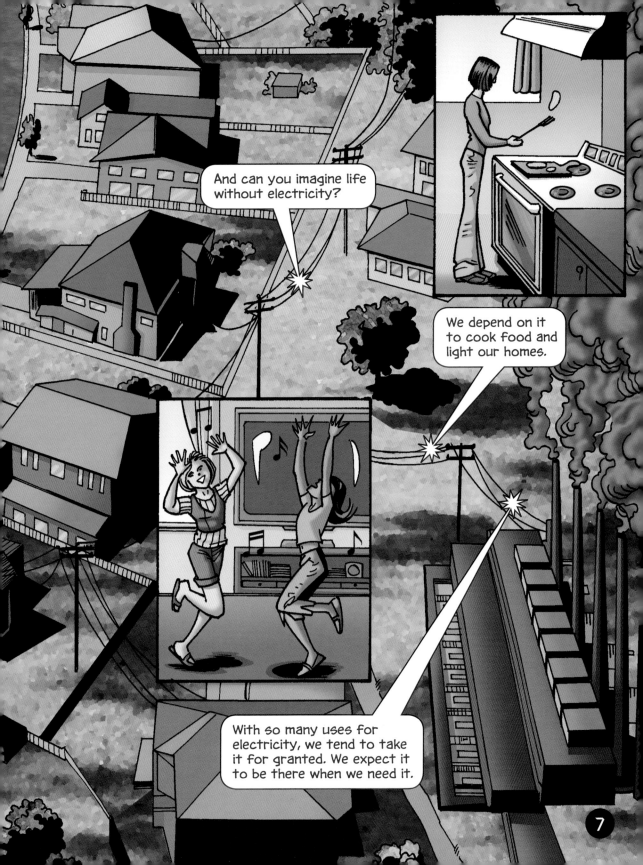

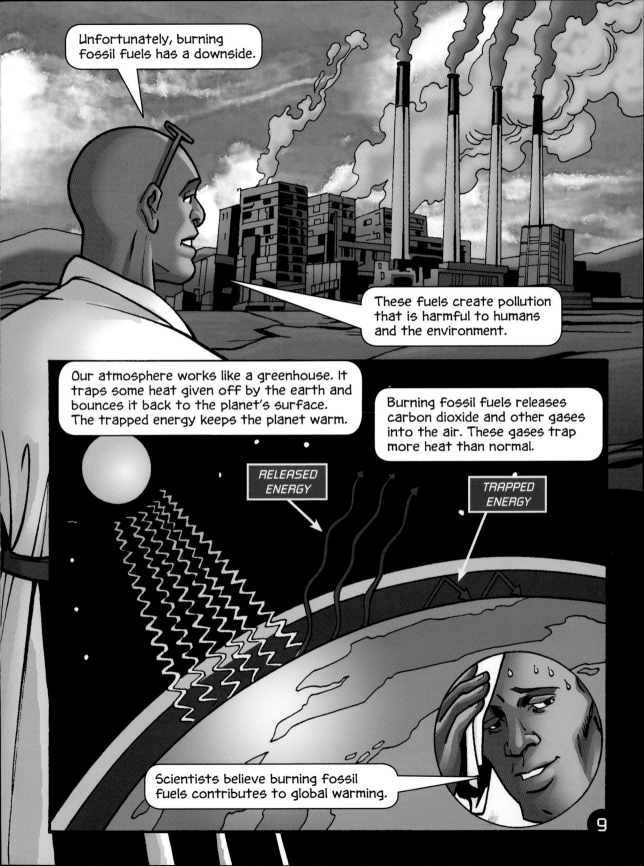

The limited supply of fossil fuels is another problem with this energy source.

Coal, oil, and natural gas are non-renewable resources. That means someday we will run out of them.

COAL

OIL

NATURAL GAS

CLEAN COAL?

ACCESS GRANTED: MAX AXIOM

Researchers have developed ways to clean coal by removing pollutants before it is burned. But pollutants such as carbon dioxide must be captured and stored to prevent them from being released into the air. Carbon storage technology is still experimental and expensive.

To confront issues like limited natural resources and global warming, people are turning to renewable energy sources.

Energy sources are found everywhere in nature. The sun shines, the wind blows, and crops grow. These energy sources are renewable.

They are all part of ongoing natural cycles. They create little or no pollution.

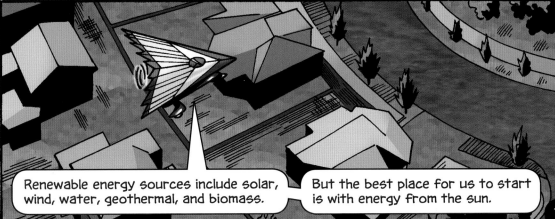

Renewable energy sources include solar, wind, water, geothermal, and biomass.

But the best place for us to start is with energy from the sun.

What do you use at night or on cloudy days?

I'm hooked up to the city utility grid. When I make more electricity than I need, it goes into the grid.

On cloudy days, I get power from my city utility.

Best of all, after buying my solar collecting equipment, the energy that powers my home is free.

And it doesn't hurt the environment.

That's right, Max. Solar energy reduces the need for coal-fired power.

Thanks for showing me around. I'd stay, but I need to get to Wales.

Have a safe trip, Max.

13

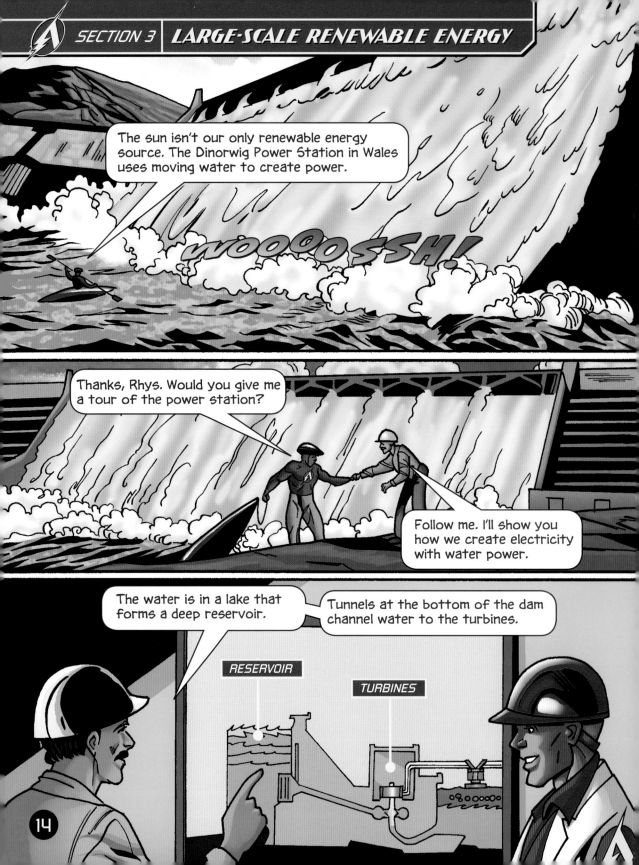

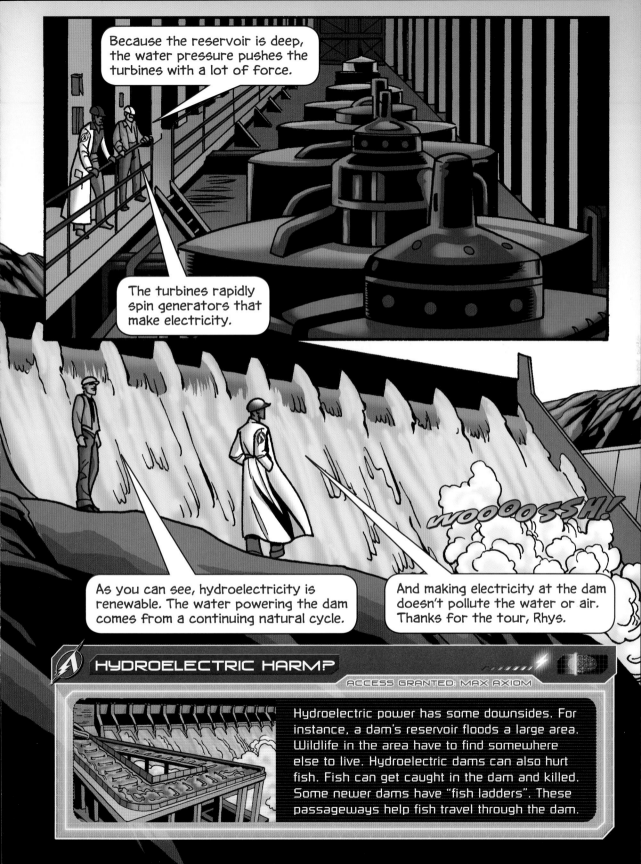

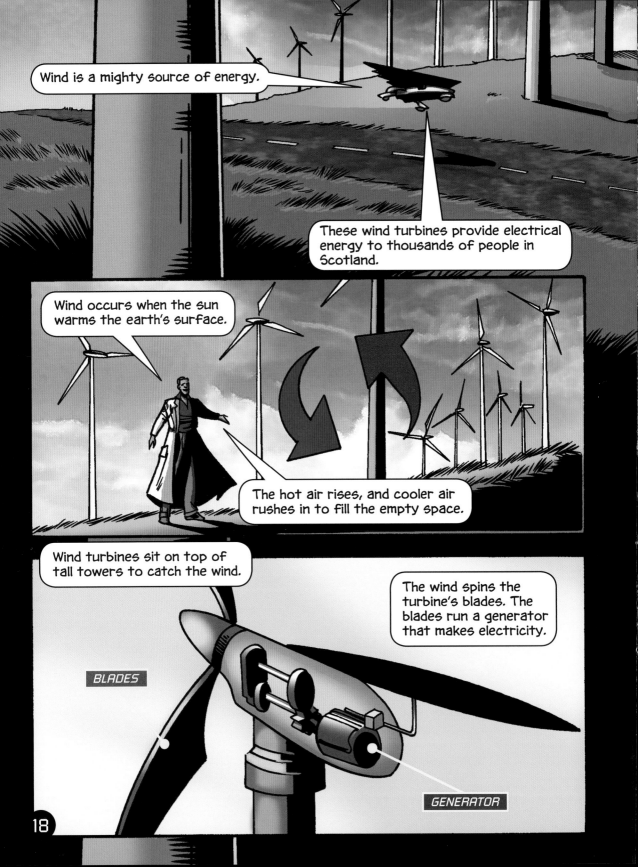

Scientists have designed different systems for collecting solar power.

This solar power plant uses curved mirrors to reflect sunlight onto a pipe filled with oil.

PIPE

The pipe carries the oil to heat exchangers. The hot oil heats water into steam. The steam turns turbines in a generator to make electricity. This solar power plant provides energy to thousands of homes.

The future of solar power is exciting. Let's find out about other new developments in renewable energy.

FOOD OR FUEL?

ACCESS GRANTED: MAX AXIOM

One downside of ethanol fuel is that it uses crops for transport instead of food. Scientists want to take the biofuel burden off of our food supply. They are working on ways to make biofuel from non-food plants and crop waste.

As we've seen, renewable energy sources can be found in unusual places.

Believe it or not, this landfill site is a good source of renewable energy too.

Plant and animal waste, such as food scraps, grass cuttings, and manure, are forms of biomass. Buried in landfill sites, this biomass releases methane gas.

When it is released into the atmosphere, methane acts as a greenhouse gas, which contributes to global warming.

METHANE DRILL

But methane from landfill sites can be burned like natural gas. It can drive turbines that generate electricity.

If we use gases from landfill sites, we release less methane into our atmosphere.

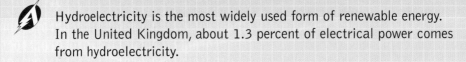

Hydroelectricity is the most widely used form of renewable energy. In the United Kingdom, about 1.3 percent of electrical power comes from hydroelectricity.

Capturing energy from the sun is not a new idea. In the 1500s, artist and inventor Leonardo da Vinci sketched plans for using solar energy to heat water.

The United Kingdom has the largest potential wind resource in Europe.

Researchers are working on putting solar farms on the ocean. But some scientists believe that solar panels on the ocean would block sunlight and upset the ocean's animal and plant life.

Almost all of Iceland's electricity comes from geothermal and hydroelectric energy sources. Most of Iceland's homes are heated with geothermal energy.

Scientists have found a way to make biofuel from algae. Algae is easy to grow and takes up less space than land crops like corn or soybeans.

In 1896, inventor Henry Ford designed his first car to run on 100 percent ethanol fuel.

A fuel cell is like a battery. It converts chemical energy into electricity. Today, fuel cells are an experimental source of power in some buildings. Car-makers are developing cars that use hydrogen fuel cells. These cars use hydrogen fuel, instead of petrol or diesel fuel, to run an electric motor.

Used vegetable oil from fast food restaurants doesn't have to go to waste. It can be recycled to provide fuel for cars. The vegetable oil is combined with ingredients such as lye and methanol to make biofuel. This "fast food fuel" works great — and it smells like chips!

MORE ABOUT

SUPER SCIENTIST

Real name: Maxwell Axiom
Height: 1.86 m (6 ft 1 in.)
Weight: 87 kg (13 st. 10 lb.)
Eyes: Brown   Hair: None

Super capabilities: Super intelligence; able to shrink to the size of an atom; sunglasses give X-ray vision; lab coat allows for travel through time and space.

Origin: Since birth, Max Axiom seemed destined for greatness. His mother, a marine biologist, taught her son about the mysteries of the sea. His father, a nuclear physicist and volunteer park warden, showed Max the wonders of the earth and sky.

One day, while Max was hiking in the hills, a megacharged lightning bolt struck him with blinding fury. When he awoke, he discovered a new-found energy and set out to learn as much about science as possible. He travelled the globe studying every aspect of the field. Then he was ready to share his knowledge and new identity with the world. He had become Max Axiom, Super Scientist.

biofuel fuel made of, or produced from, plant material

biomass plant materials and animal waste used as a source of fuel

crust thin outer layer of the earth's surface

ethanol a biofuel made from crops such as corn and sugarcane

fossil fuels natural fuels formed from the remains of plants and animals. Coal, oil, and natural gas are fossil fuels.

generator machine that makes electricity by turning a magnet inside a coil of wire

geothermal relates to the intense heat inside the earth

hydraulic has to do with a system powered by fluid that is forced through pipes or chambers

hydroelectricity a form of energy caused by flowing water

microwave wavelength in the electromagnetic spectrum

reservoir holding area for large amounts of water or steam

turbine engine powered by steam or gas

FIND OUT MORE

Books

Energy Alternatives, Robert Snedden (Heinemann Library, 2006)

From Windmills to Hydrogen Fuel Cells: Discovering Alternative Energy, Sally Morgan (Heinemann Library, 2007)

Fuelling the Future series (Heinemann Library, 2008)

Future Power (Green Files series), Steve Parker (Heinemann Library, 2003)

Potato Clocks and Solar Cars: Renewable and Non-renewable Energy, Elizabeth Raum (Raintree, 2008)

Websites

http://www.electricmountain.co.uk/dinorwig.htm

Find photos, facts, and figures about the UK's biggest hydroelectric power station on this website.

INDEX